D1191404

THE PSYCHOLOGY OF THE SICKBED

by J. H. van den Berg, Ph.D., M.D.
Professor at the University of Leiden

DUQUESNE UNIVERSITY PRESS
Pittsburgh, Pa.
Editions E. Nauwelaerts, Louvain

THE PSYCHOLOGY OF THE SICKBED is the American edition PSYCHOLOGIE VAN HET ZIEKBED which was published by G. F. Callenbach N. V., NIJKERK.

Library of Congress Catalog Card Number 66-30572
© 1966, by Duquesne University
Manufactured in the United States of America

CONTENTS

Contents

Contents

PREFACE

Many valuable comments have reached me since the publication of this book and I wish to express my appreciation for them here. That the second edition appears unchanged finds its explanation in my intention to add a few more chapters at a later date, which will enable me to discuss the suggestions I received more thoroughly than is possible within the framework of this publication.

Two observations however seem to me to be of such significance that I cannot refrain from giving a short and preliminary comment on them.

First, quite wrongly I did not discuss the contact between the nurse and the patient, so that the impression was created that I consider this contact of no real importance. That is certainly not my opinion. The nurse has a very definite and extraordinarily important meaning in the life of a patient. The hospital physician usually lacks the time to talk with the patient often enough and long enough; visitors are allowed only a few hours a day; it is the nurse who, because she is there night and day, is quite often far more intensely "with him" than the doctor or the visitors. Every nurse knows how great and how hard to bear are the responsibilities which go with this close association. She also knows that the dangers of this association are not at all imaginary. Undoubtedly it is important that this matter should be given considerable attention.

Secondly, many readers have asked me why in this psychology of the sickbed not a word was mentioned about the evangelical approach to the patient. My reply to this can be very short. It is my opinion that if an evangelical approach is not realized in the day-to-day contact with the patient, there is no sense in approaching him with religious words. For instead of approaching him, we would only be annoying him. If nothing of an evangelical approach is apparent from this psychology of the sickbed, I consider my effort a failure. So it was on purpose that I was silent on the consolation which reaches the patient from the Gospel—the only consolation which can be of real value to him. A consolation, however, which may be given only if the things which it expresses in direct terms have been embodied by the way we were previously "with him."

But it would certainly be informative to discuss the evangelical approach itself and to contemplate the exceptional task of the minister at the sickbed. I hope to do this in a future publication.

J. H. van den Berg

INTRODUCTION

In the following pages we shall deal with the problems arising from the state of being ill. We will not approach them from the medical point of view; that is to say, we will not endeavor to describe the condition in a physiological or anatomical sense, but we will observe the changes in a sick person's existence, the changes in his life which suddenly confront a person when he finds himself ill. We will watch the situation in which he finds himself when, whether or not on the advice of his

17

doctor or his relatives, he decides to go to bed to stay until he has recovered. In other words, we shall attempt to give a psychological description of the sickbed. Because the sickbed has a particularly poignant significance for those patients who fear, know, or suspect, that their hope of recovery is doubtful or futile, we shall direct our investigation mainly to the chronic sickbed, the sickbed in which the patient will be confined for a long time and which he may never leave. The sickbed which may become, or which already is, a deathbed.

A psychology of the sickbed would be incomplete if nothing were said about, and to, those who visit the patient. The sickbed and visitors are linked together. We shall see that the way the sick person, and particularly the chronic patient, experiences his sickbed depends to a great extent on the behavior of the visitor: the way he enters, the way he finds a seat and the way he talks. In the form of a few tentative words of advice—for visitors

never misunderstand their task so completely as when they think they know
it well—we shall mention the prac-
tical consequences, which, as will be
shown, evolve harmoniously from the
psychology of the sickbed. Finally, because it differs so fundamentally from a
visitor's call, we shall try to define the
characteristic qualities of the doctor's
call.

THE MEANING
OF BEING ILL

to start the day in the usual manner. But soon I notice that I cannot. I have a headache; I feel sick. I notice an uncontrollable urge to vomit and I deem myself so incapable of facing the day that I convince myself that I am ill. I return to the bed I just left with every intention of staying there for a while. The thermometer shows that my decision was not unreasonable. My wife's cautious inquiry whether I would like something for breakfast makes the reason much clearer. I am *really* ill. I give up my coffee and toast, as I give up everything the day was to bring, all the plans and the duties. And to prove that I am abandoning these completely I turn to the wall, nestle myself in my bed, which guarantees a comparative well-being by its warm invitation to passivity, and close my eyes. But I find that I cannot sleep.

Then, slowly, but irrevocably, a change, characteristic of the sickbed, establishes itself. I hear the day begin. From downstairs the sounds of household activities penetrate into the bedroom. The children are called for breakfast. Loud hasty voices are evidence of the fact that their owners have to go to school in a few minutes. A handkerchief has to be found, and a bookbag. Quick young legs run up and down the stairs. How familiar, and at the same time how utterly strange things are; how near and yet how far away they are. What I am hearing is the beginning of my daily existence, with this difference, though, that now I have no function in it. In a way I still belong completely to what happens downstairs; I take a share in the noises I hear, but at the same time everything passes me by, everything happens at a great distance. "Is Daddy ill?" a voice calls out; even at this early moment, it has ceased to consider that I can hear it. "Yes, Daddy is ill." A moment later the door opens and they come to say goodbye. They remain just as remote. The distance I measured in the sounds from downstairs appears even greater, if possible, now that they are at my bedside, with their fresh clean faces and lively gestures. Everything about them indicates the normal healthy day, the day of work and play, of street and school. The day outside the house, in which "outside" has acquired a new special meaning for me, a meaning emphasizing my exclusion.

I hear that the day has begun out in the street. It makes itself heard; cars pull away and blow their horns, and boys shout to one another. I have not heard the sounds of the street like this for years, from such an enormous distance. The doorbell rings; it is the milkman, the postman, or an acquaintance; whoever it is I have nothing to do with him. The telephone rings; for a moment I try to be interested enough to listen, but again I soon submit to the inevitable, reassuring, but at the same time slightly discouraging, knowledge that I have to relinquish everything. I have ceased to belong; I have no part in it.

The world has shrunk to the size of my

bedroom, or rather my bed. For even if I set foot on the floor it seems as if I am entering a *terra incognita*. Going to the bathroom is an unfriendly, slightly unreal, excursion. With the feeling of coming home I pull the blankets over me. The horizon is narrowed to the edge of my bed and even this bed is not completely my domain. Apart from where I am lying it is cold and uncomfortable; the pillow only welcomes me where my head touches it. Every move is a small conquest.

Change of the Future and the Past

The horizon in time too is narrowed. The plans of yesterday lose their meaning and their importance; they have hardly any real value. They seem more complicated, more exhausting, more foolish and ambitious than I saw them the day before. All that awaits me becomes tasteless, or even distasteful. The past seems saturated with trivialities. It appears to me that I hardly ever tackled my real tasks. Future and past lose their outlines; I withdraw from both and I live in the confined present of this bed which guards me against the things that were and those that will be. Under normal circumstances I live in the future, and in the past as far as the future draws upon it to prescribe my duties. Apart from a few special moments I never really live in the present, I never think of it. But the sickbed does not allow me to escape from the present.

Normally I am not aware of my body; it performs its tasks like an instrument. Now that I am ill, I become acutely aware of a bodily existence, which makes itself felt in a general malaise, in a dull headache and in a vague nausea. The body which used to be a condition becomes the sole content of the moment. The present, while always serving the future, and therefore often being an effect of the past, becomes saturated with itself. As a patient I live with a useless body in a disconnected present.

The Meaning of Being Ill

Everything gets an "actual" meaning, and this is quite a discovery for us who are pledged to the future. The telephone, rather than conveying the message from the person at the other end of the line, makes me aware of the fact that, as a frozen appeal, it rings with a new sound through a house which has become remarkably remote and strange. The blankets of my bed, articles so much devoted to utility that they used to disappear behind the goal they served, so that in my normal condition I could not possibly have said what color they are, become jungles of colored threads in which my eye laboriously finds its way. The sheets are immeasurable white plains with deep crevasses, steep slopes and insurmountable summits; a polar landscape to the paralyzed traveller that I am.

The wallpaper which I only noticed vaguely, if I ever saw it at all, has to be painfully analyzed in lines, dots, smaller and larger figures. I feel an urge to examine the symmetrical pattern, and to see in it caricatures of people, animals and things. It is as if I am taking a Rorschach-test, immensely enlarged. Hopeless and nightmarish interpretations urge themselves upon me, particularly when I am running a fever. And I feel I am going mad when I find a spot that cannot be made to fit into the structure which took me such pains to evolve.

After a few days I begin to hate the oil painting on the wall. For by this time I have acquired a certain freedom to change the caricatures of the wallpaper; I can replace the configuration I created by another one when I am bored with it. But the figures in the painting, the people, the animals, the houses and the trees, resist every attempt in this direction. The hunter, about to shoot the flying duck, remains aiming motionlessly, while I have judged his chances a hundred times. And the duck, which would probably manage to reach a hiding place if it is quick enough, defies all dangers as it comfortably floats over the landscape where the sun forgets the laws of cosmography in an eternal sunset. "Oh! please, hurry up" I say, exasperated, and even if I am amused at my own words, I do ask the next visitor to please be kind enough either to turn the picture to the wall or to remove it altogether.

The Call of Things

As I notice my clothes, hanging over the chair at the foot of my bed, I realize with a new clarity that the horizon of my existence is narrowed. For the jacket there, the shirt and tie, belong to the outside world. I see myself descending the stairs, going to work, and receiving guests. Certainly I am that man, but at the same time I have ceased to be him. The clothes are completely familiar and very near, and yet they belong just as truly to a world which is no longer mine. I feel a vague sympathy for these clothes, which remind me, tactfully, of my healthy existence, which must have had its value. Nevertheless, I am pleased when caring

31

hands change my bedroom into a proper sickroom and my clothes are put away in the wardrobe. For however tactful the reminder is, I do not like to be reminded at all. After all, I cannot and will not put it into effect anyway.

If I am sensitive this way, if I possess the remarkable sense which enables people to understand the language of the lifeless objects, the discovery of my shoes is particularly revealing, even if I find it hard to put into words what these shoes, with their silent and yet expressive faces, have to say. In his famous journal,[1] Julian Green drew our attention to the fact that it is the hat and shoes that are the most personal of our clothes. None of our clothes is entirely anonymous; they are all part of ourselves in a way, an extra skin, the skin that we choose to show others and which we want to see our selves. We choose our various articles of clothing with this showing and seeing in mind.

[1] *Journal II* (1935-1939), Plon, Paris, 1939, p. 232.

A man has not very much choice in this respect. A suit is a suit; the colors may vary a bit, the material and the cut may depend on the amount of money he can afford or is willing to spend. But that is all the variety at his disposal. A man who respects himself buys a shirt that hardly differs from the one his neighbor or colleague wears. In the matter of ties we are less restricted. The salesman shows us a rainbow of colors and an array of designs. A tie can be a very personal thing. That is why we are not really pleased to find another man wearing the same tie; it seems as if we meet an attribute of ourselves which he has unlawfully appropriated.

And then the hat. Even for men the varieties in color, shape, consistency, hairiness and handiness are almost inexhaustible. It becomes even more personal when the first newness has worn off. The hat acquires dents and creases; the brim gets a twist and a wave. These things are all signatures of the wearer and show his hold on things, his way of life. There are crying hats, proud hats, provocative hats, gloomy hats, tortured hats. And just as they tell us something about their respective owners, they certainly have something to say to their wearers themselves. Will the owner of the gloomy hat not be touched with a certain pity when he sees his hat hanging among happier members of its kind.

Shoes, too, form a very personal part of our clothing. Besides that, they enjoy the extraordinary privilege of having faces. Some shoes shake with laughter; others stare silently upon a vague distance; others again look at us full of reproach. In a store we cannot see these things yet; in their distinctive neutrality they make our choice difficult. But we have only to wear our new acquisitions a few weeks and the personality is there. As a rule their faces are not unlike those of their wardrobe-mates. After all, they are of one family. Our shoes constitute our contact with the earth; they tread on country lanes and city streets. Their route is our life's course. Now they are waiting for us, there, by the bed, a silent but futile invitation. The faces with which they look at me completely explain my condition: I no longer belong to the life which none the less is still mine; my street, my road, lies outside the horizon of my existence.

These are a few experiences of a short and harmless illness. Let us see now how a person is affected whose illness is not an incidental intermission, but a long, or even lasting, condition.

Stevenson's Ill Man

In his captivating novel *The Bottle Imp* Robert Louis Stevenson tells the story of a man with whom all went well in his life. With the help of a magical power, which lives in a bottle, he has become rich. He buys himself a wonderful house on one of the sunny islands of the Pacific. He has it furnished to his taste, sparing neither money nor trouble. And he mar-

35

ries a beautiful and charming girl who fits exactly into these surroundings. When he wakes up in the morning he sings as he gets out of bed, and singing, he washes his healthy body. On a certain morning his wife hears the singing suddenly stop. Surprised by the silence she goes to investigate. She discovers her husband in a state of silent consternation. As an explanation he points at a small insignificant pale spot on his body. He has leprosy. At the discovery of this seemingly insignificant change, his whole existence is ruined. It is no longer of any interest to him that he is a rich man, the owner of one of the most wonderful houses in the world. No longer has he an eye for the beauty of his island; this beauty has disappeared; at the most it is an accentuation of his despair. If he thought of the happiness of his marriage just a moment ago, now his wife belongs to the caste of the healthy, inaccessible to him from now on.

The Meaning of Being Ill

Discovery of a Serious Illness

Every year thousands of people make a similar discovery. The woman who, while taking a bath, feels "the lump in her breast" puts away the soap and tells herself the terrifying message that death has entered her existence. The man who suffered from constipation for a few months and who hears the doctor say that a very serious operation is necessary sees the scenes of his life change into other ones—and what a difference they make. Less disastrous but no less extensive are the considerations of the student who is told that he has to spend "a few months" in a sanatorium. And those of a housewife who hears that the condition of her heart makes it necessary for her to employ permanent help and that if she does not leave her bed and her easy chair, she may "live for years."

The beginning of every serious illness is a halt. Normal life is at an end. Another life takes its place, a life of a completely unknown nature. Although the patient may anxiously anticipate its sorrows and its sufferings, he never completely realizes what they will be. He considers this life of such low value that he cannot give it a form of its own. It seems to him that it cannot be really lived; it has to be passively endured. The patient feels beaten, bewildered, rebellious or—which is just as unfruitful—resigned. It is an experience of complete surprise, hardly imaginable to a healthy person. One suddenly becomes uncertain about things taken most for granted: the personal function in the existence of others, the necessity or even the indispensability of this function, the faith in a still unpredictable future and the faith in the integrity of the body—even if he theoretically accepts these and similar certainties, they are never *really* certain for him.

And just because access to normal healthy life is barred, this life urges itself

38

upon him with a new promise. The world grows dearer to him than ever. The little daily matters seem more desirable to him than ever before. When Bernanos' village priest[2] knows that he is suffering from an inoperable carcinoma and that his days are numbered, the world flows away from him very rapidly—the experience of lonesome isolation within a narrow horizon—but, at the same time, the world acquires a colorfulness and intimacy that amazes him. He had always believed that the attractions of earthly life had long ceased to affect him. With an incredible clarity, he remembers his healthy existence. And it is certainly not just a coincidence that the first thing that comes to his mind are the roads on which his feet trod; the road that led home from school when he was a child; the hot *route nationale* in summer and the muddy endless country lanes of his parish and finally the road he sees before him. These are suddenly an urgent incentive to

[2] *Journal d'un curé de campagne*, Plon, Paris, 1936, p. 336.

and never really holds a promise for recovery, keeps its temporary and incidental character, the healthy visitor quickly removes him from the world of his daily existence and accepts him as a *fait accompli*. Even after the first week the visitors have ceased to look surprised as they enter the sickroom, while it is just this surprise that demonstrates the contents of the patient's life. Even after a month their inquiry "How is everything?" is just as conventional as the gestures by which they put their hats on the bed and their coats over a chair. They barely expect a reply and the patient cannot fail to notice it. If he tries to explain how things are, how those things are that keep him anxiously alert and which hurt and torture him, he cannot fail to see how his words hardly reach his visitors; he can see them think of other things while trying to be interested. He can see them think: "We know, we have known it for quite a while, and we know it for the future; our knowledge even includes the slight chances of recovery or the certainty of a fatal end."

The sickbed soon becomes a fact for the visitor whereas it never really becomes a fact for the patient. The way in which the visitor talks about the life which only just a short time ago used to be his own reality, proves to the patient that he has simply ceased to be part of that life. He has become a complete stranger to the visitor, a non-participant, "just a patient." Everywhere his place is taken by others. While during the first few days or weeks it seemed that his absence would create problems, now these problems are no longer apparent. No one seems to worry about them. Things are going pretty well without him, he is not needed anymore. So little do people miss him that his absence is not even noticed. They only remember him when the calendar says that it is time to pay the patient another visit.

Of course, all this is never expressed openly; it would even be doing the visitor an injustice to assume that these things occur to him at all. He does not think and speak without sympathy; he has an honestly sympathetic interest. Yet he cannot possibly stop the patient, who is extraordinarily sensitive in this respect, from looking through his words at the harsh fact which brought the visitor to his sickroom in the first place: the fact that he is a "patient," a patient in his sickroom, outside of which life—with an "I have ceased to know you"—goes on regularly and sensibly. Whereas the noises from the street, the noises in the house, the new way in which the light filters through the windows in the morning and in which it is superseded by artificial light in the evening, the new appearance of his room with the slightly too large bouquet of flowers and the slightly too expensive basket of fruit, whereas all these things teach him that life outside his small existence has become strangely foreign, his visitors transform this strangeness into a hostile distance, if only by their coming and by their way of speaking.

This is particularly true when they are being tactful. For what else does this mean to the patient than that he has apparently become a person who has to be approached with tact, cautiously, which means, with a certain distance. He belongs to an existence having new norms, where the things that are said and the things that are not mentioned follow other rules than in the world outside. It is largely the visitor who makes this clear to him—he even urges these new norms upon him. The patient finds this particularly true when he wants to speak about his illness.

Justified and Unjustified Reserve

The visitor cannot be blamed for taking a reserved attitude towards the patient's accounts of his illness. He has a right to refuse to be involved in the particulars of this specific disease, or in the experience of the medical examination and of the treatment. It is a pity that this right is so seldom utilized. For this kind of reserve hardly hurts the patient. But he is certainly hurt when his wish to discuss the state of being ill as a form of life which is hard or impossible to bear, is declined with a trivial remark, or when his urgent questions about life and death are treated with a false optimism, as meaningless to the visitor as it is to him. Many patients suffer because they cannot discuss the problems that really matter to them. It is the healthy person who is to blame for this. It is he who goes through life with a completely unjustifiable levity in these matters.

The Contemporary Rejection of Illness and Death

We all fear death and illness. But we do not talk about it, neither to others nor to ourselves. Instead of overcoming this fear by meeting sickness and death openly as the most real possibility of our existence, instead of making contact with it

45

in a serious discussion, we escape from this discussion by acting as if illness and death did not exist.

The present social customs make this escape very easy. Reading Huizinga's *The Waning of the Middle Ages*, we learn that in medieval times sickness and death were visible for everyone. The sick walked in the streets; they sat at the side of the road. The lepers made their presence known by sounding their rattle; their processions were a visible warning of the silent processions of plague and cholera, which harassed Europe with a certain regularity. Death had an appearance which no one could ignore. If a person died, the tolling of the bells made the whole town join in his burial. He was carried to his grave, which was dug in the heart of the town, at the graveyard situated around the church. Death was present all the time and so was sickness.

This cannot possibly be said of our time. The sick are removed from our every-day life. They live in hospitals or institutions. A visitor to these centers of sickness usually notices very little of disease and death. There is singing and laughter; there is hardly any suffering to be seen. For serious patients are moved to private rooms; they are more or less sick in secret. When death arrives the other patients do not often notice anything immediately. But after a while, there are a few whispers. Death steals over the ward like a secret; it should never be seen. Occasionally a dying patient is allowed to go home shortly before the end. While the idea of letting a patient return to his family and his trusted environment for a last farewell is certainly laudable, it also means that death is banned from the hospital. Death is not allowed at this place of healing.

And even for the patient himself, death has to be camouflaged. Morphine is administered to him—of course, only to remove the pain. But the universal secret wish that death should come to a patient while he is unconscious is gratified all

47

the same. The graveyard is no longer situated in the center of the town in most countries. Particularly in the larger cities one has to make a search to find the dead. Their last resting place is outside the city, covered by a dome of green, hidden, and out of the way. Like the camouflaged municipal garbage dump—and sometimes near to it—the graveyard gives the impression of a *pleasant garden*. The passer-by suspects a magnificent country *mansion* rather than the realm of death.

The Right and the Wrong Aspects of the Rejection of Illness and Death

Of course, much is gained with all this. It is hygienically correct that the sick should no longer roam through town and country. It is a good thing in many respects that the village no longer has its idiot. It is only humane to give the sick the care they need: it would be heartless to keep narcotic drugs from them if the end is painful, too painful.

But much is threatened to be lost.

Psychologically, it is extremely dangerous to abolish sickness and death from
our daily life. Psychologically, it is far
from hygienic to remove the insane from
our everyday existence. Again psychologically, it cannot be considered altogether
a good thing that modern civilized man
lacks every contact with decay and refuse, thanks to ever more perfect tech-
niques of waste-removal. Wherever these
things happen, the perishableness of our
existence—actually the first human reality—becomes a hidden and therefore a
much more dangerous menace. Sickness
and death become catastrophes. To a
person who is completely unprepared,
they always come as a surprise.

Modern man can be compared to the
young Buddha who, being kept away
from every human sorrow by his edu-
cators, became exceptionally sensitive to
everything that did not fit in his artificial
paradise. It is certainly not just a coincidence that in our time so much is being
thought and written about anxiety and

dread. We have ceased to live with the realities of our existence which, just because of this negation, urge themselves upon us in the form of a vague dread. Dread is at the bottom of our seemingly happy and healthy life.

Troublesome Patients and Ill-Prepared Visitors

It can only be expected that modern man will be a difficult patient because the sickbed dictates to him the task for which he is least prepared: the confrontation with the vulnerability of his body and the transience of his life. Neither will he be a very helpful sickbed-visitor. For a healthy person is neither able nor prepared to speak of illness and death because, out of an ill-conceived sense of self-preservation, he has abolished every thought of these from his own existence.

Silence About Death

Compelled by his sickbed to take notice of these things, a patient may try to discuss them; for only a discussion can bring greater clarity to his thoughts. But he finds that no one can help him; often not even his doctor. The latter, like every healthy person, frequently prefers a false optimism to the seriousness which his human task—and certainly his medical task—imposes upon him, a seriousness which could really relieve this patient's heart, and his own. But he also arms himself with the medical sophism that to realize the seriousness of an illness and to consider death is always, and at any time, something that aggravates the illness and accelerates death. In connection with this, we would like to make the following remarks.

The first and principal demand medical action must meet is not to do any harm (*nil nocere*). This demand is not solely or even primarily directed toward the actual condition of the patient, but aims at his whole life. When a doctor is asked for advice whether or not a marriage should be considered and he knows that the hereditary taints of both partners make it medically certain that the children will be seriously affected, he is justified in advising against marriage, even if he knows that with this advice he is harming the present situation of the man and the woman. But he considers their lives as a whole, and because he wants to prevent these lives as a whole from being damaged, he pronounces his negative advice. Similarly, a neurosurgeon will refuse to remove the tortures of a compulsive neurosis if he has reason to believe that a lobotomy would damage the complete personality to such an extent that the gain does not balance the loss. The doctor who is convinced that his patient's sickbed will be his deathbed and who forbids himself and others to speak of these things, even if the patient emphatically asks for it, acts as if death were only significant at the time of its occurrence, as if death were a symptom of a disease rather than of life itself. But death is even a norm of life. Thus, the physician's silence is not right.

Death, Symptom of Life

Eugene Minkowski, in his *Le Temps Vécu*[4] compares life to a long march of which the last milestone represents death. This last milestone, he says, is decisive for the whole march. Our walking is a continuous communication with the end. We walk in one way when this end is far away, another when it is near; one way when it is clear in our minds and another when it threatens to disappear. However emphatically we may ban death from our lives, we actually never cease to communicate with it; it determines our way of life. The forty-year-old person is so often inclined to give an entirely new form to his existence because he realizes that he has passed the halfway mark; the new presentation of death invites him to reset his sails before it is too late. Im-

[4] Paris, 1933, pp. 121 ff.

manuel Kant lived with such iron discipline and with such a never abating sense of duty largely because death was never out of his mind. We may expect that the life of a person who convulsively closes his eyes to the reality of a personal end, is viewed differently from the life of a person for whom the *memento mori* is no longer frightening but constitutes the real issue of his life.

Death is a quality of life, *the* quality of life, the index of value of human existence. As a march is completed by the last milestone, so is life completed by death. To deny a person the right to contemplate approaching death actually means denying him the right to see his life as a whole, to live it as a complete life. If the end is reached in complete ignorance, a march has no sense, however many pleasant relaxations the way may have provided. If the goal, which caused such exertion, is entered blindfolded, a pilgrimage loses all sense, however many marvellous views the traveller may have

54

enjoyed on the way. If we withhold the unmistakable seriousness of his sickbed from him, if we do not allow him to speak of death on his deathbed, we debase the life of the human being who is about to meet his end.

Truth at the Sickbed

It should not be concluded from all this that every patient indiscriminately has to be told the truth about his sickbed. There are patients who never in any way ask for such information. There are patients who ask with such an evident fear that it can be assumed that they lack every preparation for the harsh reality of their condition. There are deathbeds on which it is impossible to make up for the neglect of a life time. So also there are deathbeds where the discussion has been going on for a long time and where it is held with such seriousness that our own seriousness would mean a disturbance of the peace in which the discussion occurs. In all these cases it is better not to say anything. But if a patient shows how much these questions are torturing him, if it is apparent that he wants to know in order to survey his life with this knowledge, in order to examine, to order and to rectify his life, if he desires this knowledge to give meaningful wholeness to his life, then it is certainly wrong, both morally and medically, to lie to him by urging a false expectation of health upon him, however much he may be asking for that as well.

It is doubtful whether such patients will die sooner if they are told the truth and if they are allowed to discuss it. But even if life would be shortened by a few hours, or days or perhaps even weeks, does not the benefit of a really human end balance this loss of time? Is it really so important to lengthen the time in a sickbed if it consists of nothing but a continued self-deception from which even the patient himself yearns to be delivered? What is more important: the length or the content of a life? Is not the overemphasized medical interest in a longer and longer average life-span an incorrect over-accentuation of one of the many medical tasks? The very pleasing statistics prove much in favor of the effectiveness of medical management, but in some respects they do not prove anything. The duty of a doctor is to save the life of his patients, to aid health in its struggle against disease. But human life is misunderstood if there is only an interest in the number of years and if medical care only includes the condition of the body.

For most general practitioners these are superfluous words. However, for hospital doctors and specialists, it seems that this is not always so. For they do not know their patients very well; they know little, if anything, of the patient's healthy life. They see him for only a short time, and the short duration of the contact has to be completely used, as a rule, for the care of the physical disease. Their reserve in discussions with patients is understandable though not always excusable. The hospital chaplain can do much good here. This does not mean that the clergyman is a colleague of the undertaker; the chaplain's duties still concern, like those of the doctor, the living person; the specific part of his task, however, is that he sees life in perspectives in which death can naturally be considered.

The Ill Mother of a Family

For mothers who are ill the conflict with the environment takes on an even uglier form when a "stranger" comes to take over her tasks. Even if her substitute is her own sister, her mother or her best friend, the noises she hears from downstairs prove to her within a few days that it is she who is the "stranger." The children cry louder, as if they want to show that all is not well in the house; or not as loud, by which they convey to the patient than an unexpected oppression is felt by the family. They come with stories about "auntie" who says that she has never seen such a mess, who for-

well-being. It is remarkable how quickly the worries which existed at home can subside then. The hospital has its own confined atmosphere; the worries of the household do not penetrate easily. The children who come to visit their mother are even further away and the husband who even at home was at a loss to know what to do, appears remarkably more awkward in a ward full of women. As soon as the visitors have gone, the ward resumes its interrupted routine. The nurses arrive with thermometers and medicines, discussions are resumed, and the ward gets atmosphere and color. Everything is back to normal. It could be said that the ward breathes again. And indeed many a patient heaves a sigh of relief when relatives and friends have disappeared, however much their visit has been appreciated, however much gladness has been felt at their arrival, and however much a next visit is being anticipated. Some visitors notice this increasing distance from home and family and are ready to blame the patient for her heartlessness. "She does not care a bit about anything" they say, and forget that it is the first step towards recovery, the step in fact which the patient was not able to make at home.

Conflict with the Bed

The third conflict—the classification is too artificial of course—is the conflict with the bed. The healthy person is accustomed to the daily change of work and sleep, of being up-and-about and of being in-bed. To him a bed is an attribute of the night which receives him again and again with the same gentleness. Every night he stretches and tries to find a pleasant spot for his arms and legs and for his head on the pillow. He erases the leftovers of the day from his mind except the most pleasing ones, or he loses himself in the unbridled fantasies of pleasantness. Sleep arrives. Sleep is the *systole*, the contraction of his existence, his coming to himself and his losing of himself within himself, and the bed is the place of this *systole*. During the evening the world contracted itself to his living-room of which the drawn curtains can emphasize the being-by-himself, or the being-together, while at the moment when he gets into bed this contraction reduces the world to the bed, to the spot where his body lies, perhaps even to that little spot where his head rests on the pillow and where he finds space to breathe.

This contraction can in no way be compared to the isolation in bed, experienced by a patient. The sleeping person is not isolated; the world is condensed within him. He "forgets" about it, he makes the world wait for him, he puts everything "between brackets." "Tomorrow" is the distance he creates between all things and himself, a distance which assures a complete rest. He lacks nothing; on the contrary he has gathered everything into a silence. To the patient the world seems to shout or even cry out, while to the sleeping person the world is quiet. It waits silently; everything will come back to him tomorrow. Sleep is the promise of the future; the promise, not the future itself, nor its anticipation. The latter would be what sleep means to those who are anxious about the future, sleep which will not come only because it contains too much of the future already. The chronic patient has nothing to anticipate. What will be coming is nothing but the bed, which can never really become a future. His sickbed is not a promise, not a waiting, but a permanent confinement. The patient does not put himself at a comfortable distance at the beginning of the night; he himself is nothing but distance, a distance of another character, not a comfortable one but an uncomfortable one.

His bed is not the *systole* of his existence. There is no *systole* for him, because the *diastole*, the expansion, the outward movement, the going outdoors, is lacking. When the healthy person goes to bed, his bed still has the qualities of "outside," if only for a moment. It smells of the wind which blew through the open windows during the day, the wind with its characteristics of summer or winter, of sunshine or rain. His bed is impregnated with a tinge of the things and occurrences of the seasons. To the healthy person it is as if he finds a trace of the decaying autumn leaves or of Spring's fertility, a trace of the cold purity of recently fallen snow or of the damp coolness of fresh dew, a trace of the warm vapor from the pavement, wet after a storm, whose far away thunder still penetrates the bedroom. Every night he makes his bed his own; he accomodates his body in it. He fills it with the warmth of his healthy body.

The patient lacks all this. However well his bed has been aired—for a moment—its warmth has never completely disappeared. The sheets are never as cool as he seems to remember from the past. The blankets retain the smell of his body, of his skin and his breath. His bed has the specific odor of his sick body. If Sartre's[5] observation that an always-present nausea reveals the physical quality of our existence is at all true then it is true here —in the sickbed where the patient is continuously confined within the aura of his own body, which has become repulsive in its diseased passivity. It is noticable even after a short sickness. After two or three days the bed has a definite odor. The smell of the sheets, the pillow and the pajamas, of everything in close contact with the patient, is a continuous reminder of an existence which knew no changes and which has become stale. For some sick persons, the odor is characterized by the smell of rubbing alcohol; for others, by that of a medicine, a hospital smell. In some cases the bed smells of urine or feces which cannot be dis-

[5] *L'etre et le néant;* Gallimard, Paris, 1943, p. 404.

guised by any amount of eau de Cologne. Is it surprising, then, that the patient revolts against his own body?

The Body

The body is a healthy person's faithful ally. At one time a mother's hand bathed it—and through her gestures he learned to dwell in it. A loving hand caressed it, and the affectionate touch gave him the wonderful knowledge that his body is good, as good as it was desired by the other person. The healthy person is allowed to *be* his body and he makes use of this right eagerly: he *is* his body. Illness disturbs this assimilation. Man's body becomes foreign to him. An intruder makes it his headquarters and it becomes uninhabitable to the sick person. An ailment governs it, and makes it a proliferating tissue, excreting organs, a troublesome sore or a disturbing tumor. The body has become unfaithful. The trusted ally has become an antagonist, a fierce enemy. The sick person has to revolt

66

against it. The caressing hand which made it his body and which perhaps still desperately tries to overcome its faithlessness, has become powerless.

The patient is acutely aware of this conflict. The healthy person is so much his body that he usually forgets about it. He passes on to it the duties it has to perform. It is those duties that tell him that he has a body. The steering wheel of his car reveals his hands to him, the pedals his feet, the slippery pavement the fragility of his arms and legs. Paper and pencil show him the dexterity of his right hand and the awkwardness of his left. And if he looks at his body, he recognizes the marks of the duties it performed. The soles of his feet are calloused, the knee is bruised, the hands are hard, sunburned, scarred, the grooves are black, and the nails are dirty. Everywhere it is proved to him that his body is an instrument, a condition. This evidence is sought in vain by the patient. His body becomes pale and spotless. The calloused areas disappear. Even the soles of his feet look rosy. The skin is thin and the blue veins make it clear to him that the significance of his body can no longer be found outside, but within the body. It is not an instrument but an object, a prey to disease. It's a thing that is auscultated, tested and palpated by the physician.

Illness as the Giver of Little Things

These four conflicts illustrate the dark side of the sickbed. There is a light side as well.

The patient who does not stubbornly cling to the memory of his healthy days discovers a new life of a surprising intensity. He becomes sensitive to little things.

The healthy person is usually so much occupied by important matters of career, learning, esteem, and money that he is inclined to forget the little things. Yet at a closer inspection he has to admit that it is never these matters which mark his life. He retains a certain sensitivity for little things. When he wishes to recall his childhood he will not be able to do it by just remembering the date of his first day at school, or his best report, or the time that he was not promoted to the next grade. Not even the memory of the first time he saw the sea will bring his youth back to him. He will have to recall the noises in the house of his parents, the chiming of the clock in the hall, the rattle of a loose tile on the roof, or the small spaces where the house began to be *his* house: the corner in the attic, the trusted domain under the kitchen table, or the mysterious space behind the curtains when during the winter the lights were turned on. Of the important matters he will notice that they are anchored in accompanying incidental trivialities: a sad message in a momentary rustle of a light breeze through the trees, the birth of his first child in the soundless descent

of snowflakes, the intimacy of his marriage in the dripping of raindrops on the
windowpanes.

The sick person acquires a new sense
for these little things. Better than any-
one, he knows the rhythm of the day:
the windows' gradual transition from
darkness to light early in the morning,
the first ray of the sun shining in his
room, the journey of the spot of sunlight
on the bed, the floor and the wall, the
busy noises of the day, the falling of the
evening and the barely proceeding still-
ness of the night. Although the new perception of these things does not include
the fact that he always liked them, in a
very special sense they do become trusted
or even dear to him. The patient hears
the clock chiming once and wonders if
it is half past three or half past four; after
waiting half an hour, he only hears one
chime, by which he knows with a sigh
that it must be half past one; and then,
after lying awake another half hour, he
hears again that the tower clock rolls

70

only one chime over the sleeping city so that the distance toward the delivering morning is prolonged with another half hour. Such a patient retains an unpleasant memory from such a night, but knows at the same time that the night has become alive for him, as much as a stubborn, willful but nevertheless familiar friend.

As no healthy person, he knows the rhythm of the year. He becomes one with the hot silence of a summer afternoon. He welcomes the fly which takes possession of his room with a few fierce sweeps and then disappears outside through the window, leaving the silence and the heat to grow even worse. To him the dark days before Christmas are more than just a shortening of the day; and the first robin is an experience leading without effort to deep gratitude. He discovers a hyacinth grow and watches over the first flight of the sparrows which he heard grow up in the noisiness of their household under the eaves.—What healthy

71

person ever saw a flower open, a cater-pillar pupate or a butterfly spread its damp wings?

Sublimation?

The visitor to whom the patient relates something of his new experiences has his own thoughts about it. "It is a relief for him," he thinks, and if others ask him how the patient is he replies that the pa-tient has accepted his condition by be-coming interested in a pot of flowers or a fishbowl. "Don't comment on it" he warns, "he will never get well anyway, and it is better this way." This misun-derstanding on the part of the healthy person has induced a certain school of psychiatry to construct the theory of sub-limation. The patient sublimates: he can-not satisfy his wishes in a normal way and finds substitutes. This theory is feeble without comparison. For no one has ever been able to explain how a desire becomes independent of the object which excited the desire nor how such a desire can as an existence devoid of mental problems degenerates into complete insignificance. Probably there is no better guarantee for a really unhealthy life than perfect health. But this only means that health and an existence without conflict are not synonymous. The really healthy person possesses a vulnerable body and he is aware of this vulnerability. This results in a certain responsibility and this responsibility is never a matter of course.

If we understand the word literally, it is true that the sick person sublimates. He elevates his existence to a sublime level. But that does not prevent him from being disappointed at the realization that he is not being taken seriously by those around him. He has to discover again and again that the distance toward the world of the healthy is very great, even greater than he thought. The sick person lives in another world; the space and time of the sickbed are dimensions different from those of our useful, busy, noisy, healthy existence (which are often insignificant).

RECOMMENDATIONS
TO VISITORS

adequately expressed in ordinary words spoken in a normal volume. Another thing the patient does not appreciate is the attempt to overwhelm him with arguments in favor of his speedy recovery, obviously prepared in advance for his benefit.

In general, it is not advisable to prepare oneself for a visit to a patient. The chances are that the prepared conversation will prevail over the topics the patient really wants to discuss, so that, although he may be taking part in a lively conversation, he is never given a chance to say what he wants to say. One thing should be kept in mind though: the visitor should always realize that the human threshold he crosses is higher than the one at the door of the sickroom. He should also be aware of the fact that the exact height of the threshold will be unknown to him until the words of the patient have made its measurement clear. Abandoning our metaphor, the visitor should try to find the patient in the latter's own world and discuss there the subjects that are significant in his exceptional existence. He should put himself in the place of the patient and, since the patient can only permit this if he is permitted in his turn to put himself in the place of the visitor, the latter should talk about himself and about his problems, exactly as he would if he were visiting a healthy acquaintance. In a word, the visitor acts normally.

Take Your Time

This does not mean that one has to stay long. It is not hard to be with a patient an hour or even longer while continuously creating the impression of being barely able to afford the time. But it is just as easy to pay a short visit while sitting at his bedside calmly and naturally, quietly talking to him so that the patient knows that the time given to him is truly and completely meant to be spent in a talk with him.

As a rule the patient has time to spare.

79

With what thoughts do we leave him if we enter in a flying hurry, mention a thousand things in a few moments and disappear through the door like a whirlwind? The patient remembers the conversation. The great difference in evaluation of this conversation by the patient and by the visitor becomes particularly clear when the latter has gone. The visitor is immediately absorbed by the innumerable events of his life but the patient is in bed and has time; he recaptures the conversation and thinks it over. He has all the time to discover its value and its deficiencies. A hurried conversation easily disturbs the time dimension characteristic for the sickbed; it leaves the patient confused, perplexed or dejected.

The recommendations enumerated here all have the disadvantage that, if carried to extremes, they are just as wrong as those which they intend to avoid. To take one's time does not mean that the pace of healthy life has to be checked completely in the sickroom. It can be extremely beneficial to the patient to have the humdrum routine of his existence interrupted by a lively discussion or by a short and brisk greeting.

Take a Seat

With this reserve, we recommend that the visitor sit down, even if he can only stay for five minutes. Everyone has experienced a discussion during which one's friend gets up from his chair and continues the conversation standing. We need not be suffering from an inferiority complex to experience such a dialogue as extremely uncomfortable. We feel an urge to stand up ourselves or to push the other person back into his chair. The original freedom of speech is lost. We are made continuously aware of the fact that the other person is delivering much of his speech to the walls so that, in order to see him, we must turn around in an uncomfortable way. This becomes even worse when he paces about the room. This is exactly what a patient experiences if the visitor remains standing or if he walks up and down the sickroom.

So we should take a chair. This means that we take off our coats and put away our hats. For to sit down without doing these things would be the same as to remain standing. It would mean that we are ready to leave at any moment.

It is better not to put the coat on the bed or to put the hat on top, as if it were a crown; for the bed is the patient's domain. For the same reason the patient usually does not appreciate it if we lean our arm or elbow on his bed. This is not to mention his thoughts when a visitor sits on his bed or drapes himself all over it so that every word the visitor utters rocks his bed. How would we like it if we were to entertain a visitor who, by means of some diabolic device made our chair vibrate with every word he said?

It is no trouble at all not to kick the legs of the bed. But do not take it for granted that no one would do such a thing. The healthy person hardly notices such things, but the patient does. The conversation becomes unbearable when the visitor, having crossed his legs, taps the bed with his foot with the regularity of a clock. This leg, moving back and forth, cannot fail to create the impression that its owner is either bored or irritated. "How do I manage to leave quickly?" is what the patient reads from this leg, which in its busy restlessness has returned to the street long ago. The same thing is conveyed to him by fingers drumming on the edge of the bed or a foot tapping the floor impatiently.

It is usually unavoidable for the visitor to sit at such an angle that the patient must twist his neck to look at him while he himself is in full view of the latter.— The patient cannot change this state of affairs. His location is determined. Perhaps he is not even able to move himself at all. On the other hand, he is just as helpless when the visitor moves his chair close to the bed and bends over the sick-bed so that his breath reaches the patient's face. It happens to all of us that we are occasionally addressed by a person who encroaches upon the decent amount of space between two people talking. We find the other person standing almost on our toes, his face almost in ours so that, however much we squint, we still only see a vague and distorted picture of his nose, his eyes and his busy tongue. His presence is too physical. This becomes even more noticeable if his corpulence compels us to assume an uncomfortable position. He breathes his—at times even moist—breath in our face and we know quickly if the speaker is a lover of spirits or tobacco.

In such a case, the healthy person has the freedom to step backward, and if the other person follows him immediately— which is usually what happens—he can place himself in such a position that the other person must remain outside the space which everyone considers his own. Or he can say, pleasantly but firmly, that he would appreciate a slightly greater distance between them. The patient lacks all these possibilities. A step backward or a strategic position remain idle wishes and he cannot and will not find the courage to give voice to the request which burns his tongue; a request which, he can be certain, will hurt the visitor and perhaps will make him decide not to reappear at the sickbed. The patient depends on the visitor's coming to him. He cannot return the compliment. He is never in an equal position. He always feels indebted toward the visitor, not the least because the latter seldom appears emptyhanded, which robs the patient even more of his freedom in the ensuing conversation. He has to bear patiently many things.

The patient is grateful, almost by definition. The person who is about to visit a patient can catch himself depending on this assumption: he goes to see a grateful patient. Even in advance he knows he is welcome. He can be sure to be received with open arms. This anticipation may easily put him in such a good mood that he tries to enlarge the effect: he chooses a book from his library to lend to the patient or he buys flowers or fruit. But he forgets that by doing all this he may be accommodating the atmosphere of gratitude in which he is going to be received rather than accommodating the wishes of the patient. How exhausting it is to be radiantly grateful for every piece of fruit, which has to be peeled, cut and distributed; for the flowers for which there is hardly any room left; and for the book which does nothing but enlarge the heap of unwanted literature and announce the moment it has to be "gratefully" returned, though barely looked at. It can be a relief for the patient when a visitor brings him nothing, nothing at all.

Do Not Forget That the Patient is Ill

That is to say: keep in mind that he may notice a distressing symptom while there are visitors and he may be anxiously waiting for them to go, so that the nurse can be called. It could be that one of his symptoms is a frequent urge to urinate. It could be that his body is so painful that to remain in one position, quickly becomes a torture. Other patients tire quickly; a conversation of more than a quarter of an hour requires too much of their strength. It is well to remember that if a patient who is running a fever has to be visited in the evening, it is particularly during that time that his temperature rises, so that in all probability the visit is not very welcome. Depressed patients, on the other hand, are generally worse in the morning while during the evening they may feel comparatively well. These patients should be visited in the evening. A morning visit to them should never be too long.

If we are not completely absorbed by what we ourselves have to say, but if we observe, closely but unobtrusively, how the patient listens and how he reacts, we cannot fail to notice when our company is no longer appreciated. We can then take our leave, by which we spare the patient the unpleasantness of interrupting the conversation and having to explain why. For that matter, it is always permitted to ask the patient if he is not getting too tired, or if he would rather have us cut short our visit for some other reason.

Do Not Take a Patient's Illness For Granted Too Quickly

Give him an opportunity to say how he feels. Have the courage to listen to his complaints, even if we know exactly what he is going to say.

Do not take his sickbed for granted; in other words, do not avoid speaking of life the way it used to be before he became ill. But try not to speak of life in such a way that he feels that he has ceased to belong to it. By the way they choose their words many visitors unintentionally convey to the patient that he is removed from life, that he no longer belongs. They speak of things which happened outside his room as if they were describing a foreign country which the patient will probably never see again. It is difficult to illustrate this by examples. For generally it is not a question of words which openly announce the removal of the patient. Rather it is a matter of intonation, of the way the visitor sits at the sickbed, the way he talks, and finally the way he leaves. With these unregisterable qualities of his visit, he enlarges the distance which the patient knows only too well and which he would love to have seen get smaller with a visit from a healthy person.

While we should not forget that the patient has a sick body, we must not forget either that he has a part in normal life; that, in spite of everything, he still has an essential part in life outside his room. In a visitor's call he likes to find the confirmation of his lawful claims to that reality which used to be completely his, and which, in a certain sense, never ceases to be his. The patient remains father, mother, husband or wife; he retains his function—impaired but nonetheless real—in day-to-day life.

If asked why they do not speak with unrestrained freedom about the things which directly remind the patient of his healthy existence, many visitors will reply that this would be too painful to the patient. It is a good thing to remember that it is generally more painful to the patient to be reminded indirectly, to be reminded in such a way that his healthy existence is taken away from him completely. The visitor can never prevent himself from reminding the patient of his health. His arrival at the sickbed is such a reminder already: an inducement to participate in healthy life, at least by way of conversation. It is wrong therefore to counteract this incentive by silence or indirect talk. The intention, of course, is not to hurt the patient, but actually he is struck where it hurts most:

again it is shown that he is an "outsider."

Never Show a Dislike of the Sick Body

Every healthy person can be sure that he has a—let us hope slight—distaste for anything relating to illness. He will probably never put this distaste into words. It can be taken for granted that he will suppress the faint disgust which overcomes him when he smells the atmosphere of the sickroom, just as he gets rid of, as well as he can, his fear of infection, which would keep him at a distance from the sickbed. It may even be that he is not aware of having this distaste for illness. Yet it may happen, particularly if he is not warned what to expect, that he suddenly shows this disgust by pointing to a protuberance of the bed and with unmistakable aversion, ask: "Is that your leg?" Or he may look furtively at the powdered face, full of crusts, of another patient and then say: "Doesn't he look awful?", completely forgetting

91

that some hidden part of the patient's body may look just as hideous.

The healthy person does well to mind his words a little. He can hurt the patient very much without wanting to do so and without even noticing it. What, for instance, will the patient think if he is greeted by the words: "Are you *still* doing all right?" What kind of thoughts does the visitor leave the patient if his final reassuring remark after discussing another patient's far more serious case is: "Well, things are not as bad with you *yet*." While the visitor—rightly or wrongly—refrains from discussing the seriousness of the patient's condition, he may evoke a train of thought completely unjustified by the patient's actual condition.

One of the forms in which the disgust for disease can hide itself is in the emphasis of one's own health. Some visitors cannot refrain from being radiantly healthy in the sickroom. They never feel

so full of life and so supple as at the bedside of a sick person, who is pitifully
short of vitality and who lacks all sup-
pleness. With a little too much ease, they
sit down on the chair which they picked
up with one hand from a far corner of the
room and placed it exactly in the right
spot, they throw one leg over the other
and speak with an eloquence which im-
presses and surprises even themselves.
Expertly and with noticeable pleasure
they move the flowers when the patient
asks them to do so. Everything comes
easy to their hands. And they cross the
room with a dance of health. If we wish
to know how the incurable patient feels
about that, we might watch the difference between his and the visitor's hand
when they happen to be near one another. The patient is very much aware of
this difference. It is unnecessary to emphasize it; but neither is it correct to
purposely reduce this difference. For the
patient cannot fail to notice our inten-

tions and the effect of such an intentional depreciation of our own health may be just as bad as the opposite.

It is Wrong to Evade a Discussion of the Seriousness of the Patient's Condition

The patient may desire to speak of it, knowing that his condition is serious and that it may end in death. If under these circumstances he feels that he can face a discussion on health and disease, and on life and death, the visitor should not evade it. If the patient has the courage, or rather—for he needs more than just courage—if he makes it clear by everything he says that he wants to know in order to use this knowledge to make his remaining days or weeks a real completion of his life, the visitor has no right to be silent. Occasionally the visitor should even speak when the end is not at all near, or when it is only a very remote possibility of the sickbed. In exceptional cases he should even speak if he knows

94

that the doctor does not approve, or when he positively forbids it. Such a decision should not be made lightheartedly, neither the decision to be silent nor the decision to speak. If we take care that our conversation with the patient is indeed *with* the patient, if we try as best as we can to put ourselves in his place and ask ourselves what we should have liked to discuss if the patient were our mother, our father, our wife or our child—what we should have wanted to discuss if this sickbed were ours—we shall not be far wrong.

Because these subjects are never discussed except on request of the patient, whether or not he says so in so many words, the visitor will not be deterred when he notices halfway through the conversation that the patient becomes downcast and cries. Nothing else can be expected. Nor is it to be expected that the patient will arrive at an honest acceptance of the seriousness of his condition unless he begins dismissing his ever-present hopes for a healthy future. It may happen that, having left the patient very depressed after such a painful discussion, the visitor suffers from a certain amount of self-reproach as a consequence; yet on the next occasion he finds the patient completely relaxed and at peace with the world.

Can it not be said that every intensification of our personal existence is the result of difficulties, sorrow and affliction? No one becomes mature unless he undergoes the crisis of maturation. No one experiences old age as a fulfillment of his life unless he deprives life of many of its desires. Marriage is seldom a real partnership without hardships. A deeper insight into the wonder of our existence, a more human and consequently a more acute way of experiencing the paradoxes and controversies which characterize our existence is always the result of an uneasiness akin to despair, and the challenge of a pressing uncertainty. Death only becomes a friend after a fierce and painful duel. Therefore, it cannot be right to reduce difficulties and sorrow to a minimum artificially. Only where the dark side of life is really present will the light side become light. A life which tries to remain on the light side all the time runs the risk of finding itself in a constant darkness.

Do Not Discuss the Patient with Others in His Presence

One of the most painful experiences of the sickbed is to discover again and again that one has become an "object." The "sick body" is a thing at the disposal of the doctor and the nurse far more than it is with the patient himself. To discuss him in his presence is more evidence to him that he has become an object. This becomes true in an even more general sense. For he is the subject of the conversation: an object with interesting peculiarities.

However, man is never totally an object, but always exceeds the facticity of

97

his existence to take part in a world of human values which gives this facticity its significance. I do not sit at my desk as an object when I write a letter to my friend in Switzerland. It is this writing, this momentary being-with-my-friend, that gives meaning to my sitting and which makes it a meaningful event. In itself sitting has no meaning. In my thoughts I am not even sitting. I am with my friend in Switzerland. It is precisely because my thoughts are not with the act of sitting that my sitting is meaningful. I do not walk in the street as an object among objects, for instance, but I do some shopping. It is not the act of walking that keeps me busy—what does, are the stores and windows. Precisely because I am occupied with the purpose of my walking does this walking become a meaningful movement. My walking becomes different when I take a stroll around the block in order to put a letter in the mailbox.

Our sitting, standing and walking

never have any meaning in themselves but become meaningful through their ends. I walk just "to take a walk" or "to go to the theatre," I sit "to enjoy myself chatting with friends" or "to work behind my desk." I stand "to be waited on" or "to cheer at a football game." We are so involved with the object of our actions—and not with the position and the movements of the body—that generally we find it very uncomfortable if we are observed by others as objects and compelled as a result to withdraw ourselves from the end of our actions. For most people writing, for instance, becomes almost impossible if another person observes the moving hand over our shoulder as an instrument which does, or does not, function adequately. The hand becomes an object to the other person and consequently it becomes an object to ourselves. It is no longer guided by the meaning with which it was occupied. As soon as it ceases to be a *"forgotten" means* and acquires a meaning of its own as a result of the attention of another person, the hand refuses to function.

Something in the same vein is experienced by the sick person if his visitors talk about him in his room as if he were an object, a plant which does not grow particularly well. As a result of such a conversation the patient feels himself becoming an object; lying there, he becomes an object for others to observe. His being in bed ceases to be surpassed by the meaning of the events which occur in his sickroom or outside, a meaning which—with the help of others—he manages to give such a form that he could be "a patient in his sickbed."

LYING AND ITS
VARIOUS FORMS

myself with the object "body" which vegetates under the blankets—my relaxed feeling is over: I have to move, I have to destroy the "objectness" of my body by a movement which allows me to leave this body again. To lie still is only possible in terms of a world which induces rest.

Lying Ill

Similarly, to lie ill is possible only in response to a world which allows, or even induces, a person to be ill and to lie in bed as a sick person, "patiently," in the way of a sufferer. To be ill is something that must be learned. This does not mean that he has to learn to accept the sad fact of living in the confined space of his bed, to accept the tremendous mutilation of his existence, for he can never learn to do that. Rather than make him a patient, this would make him a rebel until the very end of his illness. But learning to be ill means that, while "forgetting" about his sick body, the

104

patient must shape the things that occupy him in such a way that out of this form "lying-ill" follows with a kind of naturalness.

How hard it is to learn to be ill can be imagined if we remember how during a short illness life did not stop shouting at us. The noises from the street were a constant appeal to get up and about. The noises in the house seemed to be disputing our right to stay in bed. The wallpaper failed to provide a reassuring interpretation and the visitors conveyed the silent injunction, "Come on, get up." A sufferer who has learned to be ill hears in the noises from outside his room a confirmation of his right not yet to participate. The wallpaper has acquired a new aspect; the nervous compulsion to interpret it has disappeared. Now it speaks the reassuring language of respite. Visitors bring the world to the patient rather than calling him out to it. To be ill is only possible when the world has acquired a "patient," waiting aspect.

"Everything will wait for me, there is nothing to hurry me"; that is what the patient has to learn. This is his resignation.

Sleeping

We can only go to sleep by letting the world retreat quietly, by letting every appeal from it subside.[6] Our falling asleep is a response to a world moving beyond our horizon and becoming silent. Only by letting things drift away from us can we fall asleep. A person who suffers from insomnia knows this only too well: the things of his existence are not silent; they scream at him and keep him aware with their loud appeal. His tossing about is a response to the continuing whirl of the daily events. Sleep is more than a physiological recovery of an outstretched biological object. Sleep means a silencing of the world. Sleep is a condition of the room, a condition of the house, a prop-

[6] Cf. J. Linschoten, "Over het inslapen," *Tijdschrift v. Philosophie*, Vol. 14 (1952), pp. 207-264.

106

erty of the creaking of an old cupboard, of the howling of the wind in the chimney, of the rustling of the trees and of the far-away bark of a dog.

For this reason it is wrong to discuss a patient in his presence when he is asleep. Such a discussion retains its distressing, insulting, disturbing character even if one is certain that the patient cannot hear it. To speak in his room is in discord with the silence there; it is in conflict with the aspect that becomes apparent in the sleeping posture of the patient, in his closed eyes, in the relaxed expression on his face and in his regular breathing.

Lying Unconscious, Lying Dead

For the same reason it is not right to discuss a patient's case in his presence when he is unconscious. Psychologically, unconsciousness is a response too, a response to a world that has disappeared; the unconscious person is still not an "object."

Neither is a dead person. We know nothing of the world which brings a

dead person to his inconceivable still-
ness. How little we know about it becomes apparent when we see his enig-
matic smile, "that inscrutable smile of
the dead, so much in harmony with their
wondrous silence."[7] The conversation
about him quickly becomes an insult to
this smiling silence.

[7] Bernanos, *Journal d'un curé decampagne*, p. 216.

THE SICKBED OF THE
RECOVERING PATIENT

danger of being too one-sided, however, it is expedient to make a few observations on the sickbed which leads to a relatively complete or a complete recovery of the patient.

Toward a Healthy Future

It has previously been observed that it is not advisable to avoid discussing the patient's illness. However, the following should always be kept in mind. As long as there is a chance of the patient recovering—however small the chance may be—it is just as undesirable to be silent about health. This does not mean that the patient's apparently serious condition should be disregarded by holding out to him the prospect of robust health, which is too far removed and unreal for the patient to imagine. It means that we should help him as well as we can to form a future in terms of which he can experience his sickbed as a place for recovery. By helping him to picture this future, that is, by helping the patient to see a healthy any way be prepared to experience this recovery as a return to his healthy existence. In the loneliness of the sickbed he can have formed such a picture of "health" that the first quarter of an hour out of bed, or the first stroll in the garden would show him that the health he longed for is not desirable at all. Such a patient can then reverse his direction as it were; he can turn his back on his recovery and hold on to his illness. He may prefer this way of life to a normal one and persist in the state of being ill. For the sickbed, which is a tremendous reduction of a person's existence, does not only include a cessation of all the rights of health, but it can also have the meaning of a satisfaction of a desire known to us all in one way or another, the desire to live on a more comfortable and therefore less responsible level. A person in a responsible position can look at the work of a street-sweeper with intense envy. The manager who walks about in his factory when business is not

114

very satisfactory looks at his employees with the same envy.

For many people a passing illness is a very convenient solution, even if it is a highly uncomfortable state of affairs: for a while they can ignore everything—it is a breathing-spell. The duration of the sickbed, therefore, is determined largely by the attractiveness of the idea of health. Similarly, the time it takes to recover from a chronic illness depends in no small measure upon the way in which the patient has learned to "live" his future healthy existence. Frequently he has to be induced to live this future. The visitor's dance of health to which we devoted such unflattering words can be an extremely healthy stimulus here. The jolt against the bed may convey the encouragement: "You have to get up, you know." To be careful at such a sickbed, as punctiliously careful as recommended in the previous pages, could be doing the patient a very bad service. Perhaps not though: there will also be patients who will be driven out of their sickbeds most effectively by their visitors' "fine understanding" and by the prudence and the edification of their conversation.

Accordingly, to visit the sick is not an easy matter. What is good for one harms another. A word or a gesture which the patient enjoys to hear or see in a particular phase of his illness, discourages or irritates him in another phase. Yet there are far less obstacles in the way of a visitor if he arrives at the sickbed without any preconceived intentions; if he keeps an open mind as to the apparent condition of the patient. It cannot be repeated too often: it is wrong to prepare oneself for a visit to a patient in such a way that one appears at his sickbed with a fixed plan in mind.

THE PATIENT AND HIS
PHYSICIAN

within which his existence was a reality flows away; it flows on while he remains behind. The people who have significance in his life are also removed by the stream. Everything moves with time; the patient is stranded on a timeless shore. He is left behind, isolated. The world becomes an unusual, remote and strange place. And however near the visitor is to the patient, however much he is "with him" and tries to reach him in his visit, he can never completely abolish the distance and the strangeness. He always remains the healthy person who flows along with all things, who has a legitimate place in the stream of time, in relation to whom the patient has become an outsider. There is a gap between the sick and the healthy person and this gap has a frightening depth when the sick person knows or seriously expects that his illness is going to be fatal. The patient who has reason to fear that he has cancer—at the moment of the discovery at any rate, and perhaps as long as he doubts the success of the operation—cannot really be reached by the healthy person, however near and dear he may be to him in every respect. An outstanding description of all this can be found in one of Franz Kafka's little stories.[8]

The person for whom this obstacle hardly exists, if at all, is the doctor. Even before he enters the sickroom he is "with" the patient. There is no gap between them. The doctor is at the patient's side because his profession takes him to the edge of the stream which constitutes healthy life. That the medical profession has an unique position among other professions comes from the fact that the doctor does not participate in life in the same all-embracing manner as the ordinary healthy person. He exists as a healthy person outside the realm of health and sickness but, because of his profession, he finds himself in the realm of sickness, this enemy of life.

[8] *Die Verwandlung* (*Gesammelte Schriften*, vol. 1), New York, 1948.

That is why his profession is linked to that of priest. For neither does the latter take a complete part in life as it is generally lived. He has a remarkable kind of reserve, remarkable because it is this reserve which allows him to accept life without reserve. In a way he exists on the outside of life—which enables him to be in the midst of all people's lives in a much more meaningful way. He is a man, but he abides beyond the borderline which divides the human from the suprahuman. Or rather, being human, he is absolutely incapable of surpassing this borderline. His thoughts and his work draw their strength from a realm which is definitely no longer human, the realm through which, more than any other, makes human existence human in the full sense of the word.

"Affective" and "Cognitive" Contact

There is another thing that priest and doctor have in common: they "know."

The doctor knows "all" about the human body of which the healthy person generally knows very little, and of which he should not know too much if he wants to keep the integrity of his existence. It is only natural that in former times there was so much aversion to a scientific understanding of our body. It gives us a knowledge which is far removed from the completely different knowledge of our body which we need in our contact with others. A caress depends on a knowledge of the body which is and wants to be a stranger to knowledge of bloodvessels, muscles and nerves. The lover's eye teaches a knowledge which is essentially different from the knowledge of iris, lens, retina, optic nerve and brain. Both spheres of knowledge are mutually foreign; they are enemies. A long medical schooling is necessary to make these enemies live together in a friendly fashion. The dissecting room is the place of initiation into the mysteries of the purely physical, and the medical

patient's "demand" on the visitor consists of an appeal to the personal relationship, to friendship or love. In other
words, we could say that the contact between visitor and patient is a *"pathic"*
contact, an affective contact. The relationship between doctor and patient is
certainly not affective. Many patients do
not care which doctor arrives at their
sickbed. It is a matter of minor importance whether or not the doctor who is
called to the sickbed is personally known
to the patient. Several patients even prefer a doctor they do not know. It is sometimes felt as a great disadvantage when
the doctor is a good friend. A doctor's
visit is different in everything from a visit
of a friend or a lover; the demand made
on him by the patient does not consist in
an appeal to the personal relationship,
but in an appeal to skill and knowledge.
The patient is interested in whether the
doctor is skilled in his profession, es-
pecially if he suspects his illness to be
serious. The doctor has to *know*. The con-

tact between patient and doctor is a "*gnostic*" contact, a cognitive contact.

Illustration of the Difference

The difference is quite obvious if we compare a caress with a medical palpation. It is not impossible that a film taken of both movements would show identical pictures, for there is a form of palpation which consists in a gentle stroking of the skin. Yet everyone knows immediately and with certitude that two essentially different things are happening here. The caress is the embodiment of a "*pathic*" contact; it is the direct contact between two people. The one who caresses exists in the tips of his fingers and the one who is caressed is found only at the caressed spot. The caress is the emotional unification of two people who —this is the most striking characteristic of every emotional tie—do not want to "know" each other; that is to say, who do not want a penetrating knowledge of each other, but who want to retain each

127

other as a mutual personal secret. The caress, this most personal touch, is at the same time an envelopment of the caressed. It creates a borderline guarded by shame. Medical palpation has nothing to do with an emotional unification of two people. A knowing hand invades the patient's body; a skillful hand feels the secret of this body. For this hand all borderlines yield. There is no shame which leads this hand or which holds it back.

The Physician's Approach

In accordance with the "gnostic" nature of the contact between doctor and patient the doctor surrounds himself with light. In the sickroom all the lights are turned on at his request. In his surgery there are bright lights, light walls, a spotless sheet on the operating table and he himself has on a white coat. In his profession the doctor is an enemy of shadows—in every respect. He is an enemy of ambiguity as well. He demands a clear story. He wants facts and he will not let himself be kept from finding the smallest detail if it seems to him to be of any importance. He is a born positivist.

Even if it is true that the physiognomic image of most professions has been lost[9] so that in our days it is hardly possible to speak of a type, like the typical schoolmaster, minister or military man, and even though the typical doctor has disappeared, yet a doctor's visit has retained this conspicuous aspect: it is attuned to clarity and lucidity. It is directed toward perception without obscurity and toward knowledge without digression. His behavior makes this quite evident: he speaks with a clear voice. His questions are precise and do not give rise to a misunderstanding. His "hold" over the patient and with it his hold over all things consists in a knowledge of the facts, nothing else. The doctor is a realist. He has both feet on the ground. His way of walking corresponds to this. He

[9] Cf. F. J. Buytendijk, "Psychologic van de Kuisarts,' *R. K. Artsenblad*, Dec., 1951.

does not come up the stairs quietly. He does not enter the sickroom cautiously. The patient can hear from the footsteps on the stairs and in the corridor that it is the doctor and no one else. It can even be said that the nature of one's specialization often reveals itself in the sound of his footsteps. No specialist shows the fact that he has heels as emphatically as the surgeon. It is the surgeon, after all, more than any other doctor who concerns himself with naked facts. The internist generally walks considerably less noisily, and the psychiatrist—well, the psychiatrist walks on his toes even if he has flat feet.

The medical relationship is so much defined by its "gnostic" nature that for many doctors it is impossible to practice their profession with the same peace of mind on patients with whom they have a "pathic" relationship. To be at once friend and doctor is difficult for many. Even more difficult is it to be father or son and doctor. To be lover and doctor is impossible.

The "gnostic" contact should not be misinterpreted as a cold, calculating, dry and therefore heartless association with the patient. On the contrary, the knowing relationship of the doctor and his patient is a contact of great nearness as well. The doctor is at his patient's side, not in spite of his "gnostic" approach, but as a result of it. He is the patient's ally against a common enemy. It is precisely his knowing way of speaking and acting which makes the patient want his nearness. He is the "trusted" ally in the conflict with illness and death. This does not mean, however, that he is familiar. The medical contact combines a maximum of trust with a minimum of familiarity.

The visitor is the person with whom the patient is familiar; although he never becomes completely trusted, however near he may be.

131

CONCLUDING REMARKS

6

Not every sick person will find his experiences described in these observations on the sickbed. Very probably no one can put himself completely in the situation of the sickbed as represented in these pages. For everyone experiences things in a different way. Every patient begins his sickbed with his own past and with his own expectations of the future. Every patient makes his sickbed his own personal situation, which is after all unique. The description in this work is a

135

general one. It had to be a general one if it was not to become an endless enumeration of individual cases. Like every science, psychology too searches for general patterns or schemes. Without doubt, it is required that they resemble experienced reality as much as possible, although they will never completely cover individual cases. The purpose of the work was exclusively to give a general description of the state of being ill. A specific psychological method was used because of its broader opportunities to form an idea of the changes in the world of the patient.

It stands to reason that the patient who reads this will discover obvious deficiences and determine that important details are lacking. I am no patient and I know the sickbed only as a visitor and as a doctor. Any comments from patients will be highly appreciated, as will be those of nurses who, on the basis of their experience, wish to offer suggestions for changes or additions.